Gakuen ALICE

Volume 8   Tachibana Higuchi

Gakuen Alice

Contents

Volume 8

Created by Tachibana Higuchi

HAMBURG // LONDON // LOS ANGELES // TOKYO

Gakuen Alice Volume 8
Created by Tachibana Higuchi

Translation - Alethea & Athena Nibley
English Adaptation - Jennifer Keating
Retouch and Lettering - Star Print Brokers
Copy Editor - Shannon Watters
Production Artist - Rui Kyo
Graphic Designer - Al-Insan Lashley

Editor - Lillian Diaz-Przybyl
Print Production Manager - Lucas Rivera
Managing Editor - Vy Nguyen
Senior Designer - Louis Csontos
Director of Sales and Manufacturing - Allyson De Simone
Associate Publisher - Marco F. Pavia
President and C.O.O. - John Parker
C.E.O. and Chief Creative Officer - Stu Levy

A **TOKYOPOP** Manga

TOKYOPOP and ⟨logo⟩ are trademarks or registered trademarks of TOKYOPOP Inc.

TOKYOPOP Inc.
5900 Wilshire Blvd. Suite 2000
Los Angeles, CA 90036

E-mail: info@TOKYOPOP.com
Come visit us online at www.TOKYOPOP.com

ISBN: 978-1-4278-0326-9

First TOKYOPOP printing: July 2009
10 9 8 7 6 5 4 3 2 1
Printed in the USA

Pweeenn!

"To everyone kind enough to buy Gakuen
Alice volume eight: if you like, please check
out "Gakuen Alice vol. 7.5: Official Fanbook."
It has a story about me and Hotaru-san. I'd be
even more happy if you would read it before
reading this volume!" is what the pig over there
told me to say. *sigh* It makes no sense.

★ NATSUME HYUGA ★

MIKAN'S ARCH-NEMESIS AND THE INNATE GENIUS OF THE ELEMENTARY DIVISION. A BOY OF MYSTERY, HE SHUTS OUT EVERYONE BUT HIS BEST FRIEND, LUCA. POSSESSES THE ALICE OF FIRE. ABILITY CLASS: DANGEROUS.

★ HOTARU IMAI ★

MIKAN'S BEST CHILDHOOD FRIEND. SHE'S A COOL, COLLECTED PRODIGY, BUT SHE'S SURE GOT A MOUTH ON HER. POSSESSES THE ALICE OF INVENTION. ABILITY CLASS: TECHNICAL.

★ NARUMI-SENSEI ★

THE TEACHER WHO DISCOVERED MIKAN'S ALICE. POSSESSES THE ALICE OF HUMAN PHEROMONE.

★ LUCA NOGI ★

...SESSES THE ALICE ...ANIMAL PHEROMONE; ...Y FOR HIM, HE ...S ANIMALS. HE'S ...T FRIENDS WITH ...UME, BUT HAS ...NTLY SOMEHOW ...LOPED AN INTEREST ...KAN (?). ATTRIBUTE ...SS: SOMATIC.

our Heroine!

I'M MIKAN SAKURA. LET'S MEET THE CAST!

★ YUU TOBITA ★

THE TIMID, KINDHEARTED CLASS REPRESENTATIVE, WHO IS ALWAYS WILLING TO HELP. POSSESSES THE ALICE OF ILLUSION.

...RE SHOUDA ...ENT OF ...TSUME-LUCA ...B. SHE'S VERY ...G-WILLED, ...CONSTANTLY ...G HORNS WITH ...POSSESSES ...ICE OF CAT- ...TRIBUTES.

★ MIKAN SAKURA ★

A CHEERFUL GIRL WHOSE MOTTOS ARE: "NEVER SAY DIE!" AND "IF AT FIRST YOU DON'T SUCCEED, TRY, TRY AGAIN!" POSSESSES THE ALICE OF NULLIFICATION. ABILITY CLASS: SPECIAL.

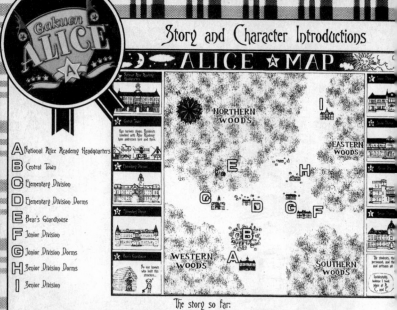

Gakuen ALICE

Story and Character Introductions

ALICE ★ MAP

NORTHERN WOODS

EASTERN WOODS

WESTERN WOODS

SOUTHERN WOODS

A National Alice Academy Headquarters
B Central Town
C Elementary Division
D Elementary Division Dorms
E Bear's Guardhouse
F Junior Division
G Junior Division Dorms
H Senior Division Dorms
I Senior Division

The story so far:

★ CHILDHOOD FRIENDS MIKAN AND HOTARU WERE BROUGHT UP IN A SMALL VILLAGE. WHEN HOTARU TRANSFERRED TO THE ALICE ACADEMY FOR PEOPLE WITH MYSTERIOUS POWERS (OR 'ALICES'), MIKAN FOLLOWED HER! HER SCHOOL LIFE'S ROCKY SOMETIMES, BUT SHE'S TRYING HARD TO LIVE BY HER MOTTO: "NEVER SAY DIE!"

★ WITH THE ALICE FESTIVAL SAFELY CONCLUDED, CLASS PREZ TOBITA GOES BACK HOME FOR A WEEK. AS HE'S RETURNING, HE HELPS A WOMAN WHO STUMBLED--ONLY TO HAVE HIS ALICE STOLEN IN RETURN!

★ THE ONE WHO STOLE TOBITA'S ALICE IS AN AGENT FROM THE MYSTERIOUS ORGANIZATION "Z." MIKAN AND HOTARU TRY TO LOCATE SEVERAL Z MEMBERS WHO INFILTRATE THE SCHOOL, BUT ARE SHOT AT INSTEAD. HOTARU IS INJURED AND IN CRITICAL CONDITION.

★ MIKAN, NATSUME, LUCA, AND TSUBASA GO THROUGH A MYSTERIOUS WARP TUNNEL IN THE SENIOR DIVISION TO FIND Z'S HIDEOUT, RETRIEVE TOBITA'S ALICE AND GET SPECIAL MEDICINE FOR HOTARU.

★ WHEN THE FOUR FINALLY MAKE IT TO THE HIDEOUT, Z'S MEDUSA (WHOSE ALICE TURNS THINGS TO STONE) AND THE MYSTERIOUS WOMAN YUKA AZUMI ARE WAITING FOR THEM. SUDDENLY, MIKAN BECOMES PREY TO AN ANT LION...?!

What is Alice Academy?

THE ULTIMATE TALENT SCHOOL THAT ADMITS ONLY SPECIAL PRODIGIES WHO POSSESS MYSTERIOUS POWERS CALLED "ALICES." EXTREMELY STRICT, THE ACADEMY RESTRICTS STUDENT CONTACT WITH THE OUTSIDE WORLD--INCLUDING PARENTS!

Questions from the Fans!

About Shouda-san and her crush on Luca--if she activated her Alice, wouldn't she be enthralled by Luca-pyon's animal pheromone even more? (Since she's a cat-dog.) And would Luca-kun swoon over Shouda-san? (Since he has animal pheromones...)

HMM--STILL, IT MIGHT BE NICE IF LUCA-KUN WOULD SWOON OVER ME...

WE'RE NOT ANIMALS, Y'KNOW!

HEY! MY LOVE FOR LUCA-KUN AND NATSUME-KUN IS PURE AND BEAUTIFUL! LOVE!!

Glance...

-kun's
g funny.

YOU'RE THAT Z INVADER....!

I NEVER DREAMED...

I HEAR YOU HAVE A NULLIFICATION ALICE.

AND YET THEY'RE FLOODING ME.

I THOUGHT I'D ERASED THESE FEELINGS...

I NEVER ONCE DREAMED THAT SEE HER AGAIN

AND I WAS CONVINCED I'D ERASED THEM FROM MY HEART.

Read at your own discretion.

Higuchi's Room 1

Hello! This is Higuchi.

Hot enough for ya?!

First short-sleeve version

Thank you very much for buying volume eight!

This volume finishes the Z Arc. It sure was long...

I got a lot of letters saying, "Please get back to the usual bright, happy plotting soon!"

Not flattering after all, so back to long sleeves...

But there really was a lot of information that I wanted to bring up in the Z Arc that's important to the future story, so I'm glad I drew it.

I got a lot of letters saying, "Anyway, just have Hotaru in it more," too, but I'm glad I drew it.

I'll draw a lot of bright, happy stories again after this!

Serious parts, too, of course.

I'll keep working hard to make a work that you can all enjoy endlessly!

The anime broadcast has finished, too. Good work making such a wonderful show, staffers!

For those of you who didn't get the channel, watch the DVDs, 'kay? Buy them, 'kay?

Please go to two.

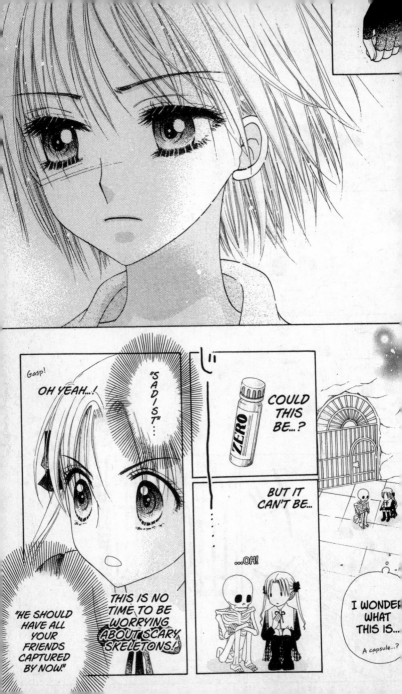

Gasp!

OH YEAH...!

"SADIST"...

COULD THIS BE...?

BUT IT CAN'T BE...

...OH!

A capsule...?

I WONDER WHAT THIS IS...

"HE SHOULD HAVE ALL YOUR FRIENDS CAPTURED BY NOW!"

THIS IS NO TIME TO BE WORRYING ABOUT SCARY SKELETONS!

ZERO

NATSUME!

WHEN I LOOK AT NATSUME...

Shiki!

...I SUDDENLY REALIZE.

hey negate each other, hm?

ARE YOU TWO OKAY?

I REALIZE HOW DIFFERENT...

NATSUME! YOU'RE BLEEDING...

ATSUME'S FE HAS EN FROM MINE.

DON'T WORRY.

I...

"I WANT TO PROTECT EVERYONE."

I CAN PROTECT MYSELF.

I DON'T NEED YOU TO PROTECT ME.

WITH MY NULLIFICATION

I WANT TO PROTECT EVERYONE, EVEN IF ONLY A LITTLE, FROM ALICE ATTACKS.

INSTEAD...

LET ME HELP YOU.

IT'S WHAT I CAN DO.

36

Chapter 42

There's an unexpected amount of people who like the way these two tease each other, so I tried drawing it in honor of Tsubasa being on the cover (or because I just didn't have anything else to draw). There are quite a few people who like the way Naru and Mikan play with each other, too.

PROFILE 26

I'M SURE BLACK CAT...

...THAT WOULD MAKE THINGS EASIER ON YOU, TOO.

WHA...?

EASIER

UNFORTU-NATELY...

MY ALICE ISN'T STRONG ENOUGH...

...TO STEAL THE ALICES OF ALL FOUR PEOPLE HERE AT ONCE.

Yuka Azumi

Born 7/14   Age 29
Cancer   Blood type O

Mikan's mama. I think she'll show up again sometime in the future. I imagine her as someone who is tossed around by the whims of fate; she's hurt, she struggles and suffers, but she keeps moving forward. When her relationship with Mikan was revealed, more readers started cheering her on, saying: "Yuka-san breaks my heart." I hope I can someday draw an episode from when she was a student with Naru and Sensei.

Go to three, please!

!!

......!

RUN...!

NATSUM

Peeh...!

Hehheh...

IT WILL BE DIFFICULT TO USE YOUR ALICE PROPERLY LIKE THAT.

YOU CAN' USE YOU DOMINAN ARM, CAN YOU...?

THERE, NOW. THE WALL IS BEGINNING TO CRUMBLE.

"EVERYONE'S WAITING FOR YOU."

WHaP!

ATSUME!

Hff...

Haah...

Hanh...

Chapter 42 / End

Higuchi's Room 3

HEY! THE GROUND'S GIVING WAY!

AND THE ENTRANCE IS CLOSING TOO!

GIVE UP AND COME BACK, BOTH OF YOU!

MIKAN!

HOTARU ...!

Reo Mouri

Born 8/20   Age 23

Leo   Blood type B

I saw Reo-sama playing a great role in the anime, and it reminded me that I'd forgotten to write his profile. He sings and stuff in the anime; I was shocked⊿. I imagine him as being kind of like the youngest kid in the family, who has a father complex and a brother complex. Never mind whether or not that's actually the case... He seems to know something about Mikan's mother; he might make a cameo and reveal it. Or not--I don't know.

PENGY...?

MIKAN...

SENPAI, PENGY...

......

PEN--

SAKURA...

I'M... I'M GOING BACK TO HELP PENGY.

MIKAN.

PENGY...

Pweeenn!

NARU-SENSEI...

OH...

That.

THOSE "TEACHERS WHO SUSPECT," LIKE SAKURANO-SAN WAS TALKING ABOUT...

IS IT WHO I THINK IT IS...?

Him?

MMM, WELL, THERE'S NO SIGN THAT HE'LL COME DIGGING ANYMORE FOR NOW.

For some reason.

AT ANY RATE, ALL WE CAN DO IS WAIT AND SEE.

But it's creepy.

AS USUAL, HE DOESN'T MAKE ANY SENSE-- LIKE WE CAN'T GET A HOLD ON HIM.

WHAT'S GOING ON WITH HIM, I WONDER?

Chapter 44

EH?

HOTARU'S SPECIAL MEDICINE...

WE ASKED HER BRO-THER, THE PRINCIPAL... TO MAKE SURE TO GIVE IT TO HER.

AND PENGY...

Higuchi's Room 4

PROFILE 28

Assistant-sensei!

Born 11/11   Age 25

Scorpio   Blood type A

I'd always been forgetting to write this (oy). This is Assistant-sensei, who I remembered only after my editor reminded me. Unlike Mind Reader-kun, he's a sad person, and I almost never get asked his real name (actually, it would really be a problem if anybody did). He's actually modeled after someone. Not a famous person or anything--someone I know. I especially referred to that person's wimpiness. I hope he becomes full-fledged soon.

Go to five, please.

IT'S ENOUGH FOR ME THAT YOU ALL...

PREZ...!

But...

...CARED ENOUGH... TO DO THAT FOR US, MIKAN-CHAN.

PREZ

THANK YOU, MIKAN-CHAN.

THESE TEARS EVERYONE IS SHEDDING...

...EY'RE BECAUSE ME BEING WEAK.

I TRIED...

...TO JUMP INTO IT ALL AT ONCE.

TSUBASA-SENPAI BEING SO MUCH MORE GROWN-UP...

AND HOTARU AND NATSUME AND EVERYONE'S STRENGTH AND KINDNESS...

THEY'RE THE RESULT OF OVERCOMING LOTS OF DIFFERENT THINGS, AND GETTING STRONG ONE STEP AT A TIME...

GET IT TOGETHER.

Here!

Sniff

DON'T MAKE PREZ SADDER WITH YOUR BLUBBERING.

ERK...

Curly...

You're gross!

Sniiiff

YOUR NOSE!

BLOW IT! REALLY!

FOR WHEN THAT TIME COMES SOMEDAY.

IT'S NARUMI-SENSEI.

Sniff

Honk

NE UND T.

UT NO 'S SEEN ARUMI-ENSEI E THEN.

HUH?

WE WERE ALL CONFINED TO THE DORMS FOR NOW.

Until Sensei gets back.

OH YEAH, MIKAN-CHAN...

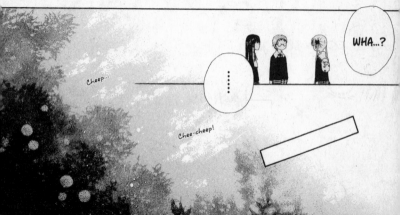

Cheep...

......

Chee-cheep!

WHA...?

"I JUST WANT TO CREATE A WARM HOME WITH SOMEONE I LOVE."

"YOU KNOW, MY DREAM..."

"...IS A REALLY TINY DREAM."

"TO SOME, IT MIGHT BE A SIMPLE, BORING THING..."

"BUT TO US ALICES, SUCH A SMALL THING SEEMS LIKE A FAR, FAR OFF FANTASY RIGHT NOW..."

"SENSEI?"

"DO YOU THINK DREAMS COME TRUE?"

"THEY DO."

"IF YOU DON'T GIVE UP."

．．．．．

NARU...

LONG TIME, NO SEE, YUKA-SENPAI.

...YOU, TOO, SHIKI-SAN.

I KNEW IT.

I KNEW I'D SEE YOU IF I WAITED HERE.

...SHE REJECTED ME.

SHE GLARED RIGHT AT ME.

"GIVE TOBITA'S ALICE BACK!"

[W]AT IS MY [DA]UGHTER, [ALL] RIGHT.

"FIX HOTARU!"

WITH ALL HER BEING...

HER EYES WERE SO SIMILAR I COULDN'T STAND IT.

[S]HE HAD...

THE SAME ALICE HE DID...

"I'M SURE YOUR DREAM..."

"...WILL COME TRUE."

Gyaaa! How embarrassing! What a lame pun!

WHA...?! WHAT ARE YOU SAYING, SENSEI?

HUH?

WHEN IT DOES...

[WH]AT? YOU [SAI]D THAT [WE/NA]ME ARE [PERF]ECT FOR [EAC]H OTHER.

"YUZU" AND "MIKAN." THEY'RE NAMES OF SIMILAR FRUIT, PERFECT FOR A FRIENDLY MOTHER/CHILD RELATIONSHIP.

YOU SHOULD NAME YOUR CHILD "MIKAN." RIGHT?

Gr.

BECAUSE YOU...

I'LL NEVER...

...BE ABLE TO RESPOND TO YOUR EARNEST-NESS, EVER.

YOU WERE TOO INTENSE.

...SENPAI.

SINCE THAT DAY...

...I'VE KEPT LOOKING FOR YOU.

SO I WANTED ...

MY HEART WAS HOLLOW.

I DIDN'T CARE ABOUT ANYTHING.

I WANTED TO SEVER MYSELF FROM YOUR FUTURE.

NOT YOUR INTENTIONS...

...OR SENSEI'S DREAM.

THOSE
FEELINGS
YOU STOLE
FROM ME...

ALL I WANTED...

...WAS TO GET BACK
THE FEELINGS OF
LOVE THAT SHOULD'VE
BEEN THERE.

S E N P A I.

...WERE MY
WHOLE
LIFE'S
WORTH OF
LOVE.

THANKS TO
YOU, EVER
SINCE THAT
DAY...

...I'VE RETREATED
INTO WHO I WAS
BEFORE I UNDER-
STOOD LOVE
OR ROMANCE.

TO CUT OFF MY
ATTACHMENT
TO YOU.

YUKA-
SENPAI.

*I WAS SUPPOSED
TO BE HOLLOW, BUT...*

Chapter 44 / End

NARUMI-
SENSEI...

Chapter 45

Gakuen ALICE

Higuchi's Room 5

PROFILE 29

Pweeenn!

Pengy

Born: Summer
Age: 1?

Lucky Pengy, of whom I am often asked: "He's not gonna be in it anymore?" Thank you for all the many letters you sent at his conclusion. It would have been nice if I could have had him in it the whole series as the Gaku-Ali mascot character, but I had planned for his end from the beginning, so unfortunately, he has to say goodbye. I'm sorry. I get the feeling that when my assistants would lay the tone for Pengy, they would make strange "Peeeh" noises. Come to think of it.... I think it would be nice if the day comes when he can see everyone again in some form. Pween.

People he likes:
Hotaru, Mikan, Luca

People he likes well enough:
Tobita, Tsubasa, Nonoko, Anna

People he doesn't really like:
Natsume, Curly

Please go to six.

PENGY.

"I WANT YOU
RETURN TH

Read at your own discretion.

Go to seven, please.

ALICE
STONES...

YUKA.

I WONDER IF HOTARU-CHAN IS ALL BETTER.

AND HERE'S ME GOOD 'S TODAY, TOO.

I'M SURE SHE IS!

Mikan-chan and the others worked really hard to get the medicine for her.

I HEAR TOBITA'S ALICE CAME BACK SAFE!

HAT'S A RISE, IT COMING ALL OF UDDEN.

ow?

We were so worried!

Oh, good!

We were so scared!

Waaahh!

Eeeep! Stop!

We love you!

TOBITA!

Congratulation

Mentaiko Pillow

AND THE OTHER TWO FROM THE JUNIOR DIVISION WHO HAD THEIR ALICES TAKEN GOT THEM BACK ON THE SAME DAY.

For reasons unknown.

NEITHER US NOR THE ACADEMY UNDERSTANDS MUCH ABOUT IT YET...

It's a miracle!

We're so glad!
We're so glad!
We're so glad!
We're so glad!

IT'S JUST, WHILE I WAS SLEEPING...

WELL, WHATEVER HAPPENED, IT DOESN'T CHANGE THE FACT THAT IT'S AWESOME.

Way to go!

YES!

Thank you, everyone! Really!

It's like a dream...

BEFORE I KNEW IT...

Whoa!

What is it...?

AH!

EEP?!

HOTARU.

HOTARU...

HO--

HOTARU
...

HOW MANY
TIMES DO YOU
HAVE TO SAY
IT BEFORE
YOU'RE DONE?

I know my

FIRST NATSUME HYUGA...

WE CAN'T SIT BACK AND IDLY WATCH WHILE A MEMBER OF OUR FACULTY INDEPENDENTLY FLITS ABOUT LIKE THAT.

Regardless of whether or not it becomes public knowledge.

HYUGA-KUN ONLY NEEDS ANOTHER SEVERE PUNISHMENT.

...NOW NARUMI-SENSEI, TOO?

NOW, THE PRO-BLEM...

IS HOW O DEAL TH THIS T, NARUMI-SENSEI, N THE UTURE...

AS FOR NATSUME HYUGA, THAT WAS DUE TO MY NEGLIGENCE AS HIS SUPER-VISOR...

YOU'RE NOT GOING?

"TSU-BASA."

DON'T YOU MEAN "TSUBASA-SENPAI"?

Feh.

Natsume! Where are you going?

Chapter 45 / End

Chapter 46

THANKS

THANK YOU SO MUCH FOR READING THIS FAR.

SPECIAL THANKS

Nakamura-san, Tamura-san, Ida-san, Akao-san, Kasai-san, Matsuura-san, Sugino-san, Ogawa-san, Family-san, Friends-san, Editor-san, and all my readers.

SEE YOU AGAIN

I hope to continue making manga you enjoy!

AND AFTER THAT, WE ALL MADE A SNOW DOLL AND HAD A FAREWELL PARTY FOR PENGY.

ON THAT D—
WE ALL W—
OUTSIDE—
PLAYED A—
HAD SNOW—
FIGHTS A—
STUFF—

...GRANDPA...

HOTARU SAID QUIETLY, "EVEN IF I DID, IT WOULDN'T BE LIKE THE PENGY THAT SPENT ALL THAT TIME WITH US WOULD COME BACK."

WHE—
SOMEO—
ASKE—
"WILL 9—
MAKE P—
AGAIN—

Read at your own discretion.

Higuchi's Room 7

Higuchi hasn't been into games since Super Nintendo; she's slow, and gets tired and stops right away.

One day, I was playing the Gakuen Alice GBA game.

It's so fun...

Beep Beep

Actually, I've only played it twice, and I'm a wimp who's never made it to the end...

Exactly the same →

Ah ha ! Mikan's a moron!

When I play it, I can see my own characters objectively: it's fascinating.

Beep

Natsume's so twisted.

Beep

What's with her...? She's so blunt. So cold...

Ho... Hotaru...

But the problem was Hotaru...

You're so noisy

Grrr! That hurts!

Stupid

Beep

What's your problem, Hotaru? Treat her more kindly, you mean-ie!

Beep Beep

I'm impressed with Mikan... She keeps going after Hotaru without giving in to her poisonous attitude...

Glass Heart...

It was an afternoon that made me realize that it's fun to draw Hotaru, but if she was actually my friend, it would be tough to get along...

The M in Mikan stands for Masochist.

If there's anyone who likes people like Hotaru in real life, they are definitely masochists... Hotaru was supposed to be my favorite character...

It's the end.

HEY! KIDDOS!

YAY!! I FOUND TSUBASA-SENPAI!!

And Misaki-senpai and Glasses-guy!

AH! TONO-SENPAI'S HERE, T...

It's only you now, Riko-san.

You sweet-talker, you, Akira-kun.

MMPH MPH...!

YES, YE(S) MIKAN-CH(AN) LET'S G(O) OVER THE(RE)

There's lots (of) fun stuff

Is this two's timing with a nurse?

AH...

BUT WE THOUGHT WE'D AT LEAST GET HIM PRESENTS...

"MIKAN"

...IS SOMETHING YOU CAN'T FORGET.

NATSUME'S DONE A LOT OF STUFF TO HELP ME, TOO.

MAYBE I'LL GIVE HIM SOMETHING, TOO.

OH, THERE YOU GO, OVERREACHING WHEN YOU'RE SO VERY POOR...

Don't bite my style!

Shut up, Curly!

I will bite you!

I SEE.

THE BIRTHDAY OF SOMEONE YOU REALLY LOVE...

BUT THE MORE IMPORTANT THAT PERSON IS...

...THE MORE IMPORTANT THAT TIME SPENT FEELS.

I CA IMAG NATS LOOK HAP

But it's for t

BUT CHOO: PRESENT A THINKING A WHO YO GIVING IT

I thi bein

AND WON- DERING, "SHOULD I GET THIS? WHAT ABOUT THAT?" IS REALLY HARD.

ぽつん…

Sleepy...

"DON'T GO THINKING ANYTHING LIKE..."

"...I MIGHT BE FREE SOME- DAY."

か け

"...N.A.T.S.U.M.E."

HMMM, A DRAWING OF NATSUME-KUN, EH? ♡

...d job, ...chan.

Fo' you...

A present...

For Nastumay-kun

...HAPPY BIRTHDAY.

...now, no ...illing for ...ur own.

From left-field...

...a formidable opponent appears...

Erk...

...THANKS.

LOOKS LIKE THAT ONE'S FROM LUCA-KUN.

NOW THEN! ♡

ALL YOU HAVE TO DECIDE IS WHICH ONE IS THE LOSER.

Here you go! NATSUME-KUN.

THIS IS A BIRTHDAY PRESENT FROM ME! ♡

You're ignoring Yo-chan's orders?

Well, I probably won't be the loser, but I might not mind taking an order from Luca-kun. ♡

Aaaaugh, I don't want to be the loser!

SO THEY REALLY WERE PLOTTING SOMETHING.

NATSUME-KUN! THIS PRESENT IS FROM ME!

Eeek! Moron.

A MAKEUP SET FOR BOYS. ♡

Now you'll have no problem maintaining your eyebrows!

NATSUME-KUUUUN! ♡

THIS PRESENT IS FROM ME! A LOCKET WITH A PICTURE OF ME INSIDE...

You can Have it, too! Manga hair Mousse

Saya ### hair

Use it, okay? Okay?

Isn't it cool?

I thought a lot of things might be wearing you out...

Gift of a healing CD made by healers

Mine's an anti-gravity skateboard!

Now we can fly together!

Alice SKY TYPE

THIS IS THE ONLY THING I COULD THINK OF THAT YOU MIGHT LIKE, NATSUME, SO...

EH HEH!

EVERYONE TO HELP, SC A LITTLE AG THE RULE

So I don't mir
I don't get first

IT'S YOUR BIRTHDAY, AFTER ALL, SO WE HAVE TO MAKE SURE TO LEAVE FUN MEMORIES WITH EVERYONE.

NOW, EVERYONE GET TOGETHER!

Quickly!

SMILE!

YES, THAT'S A WONDERFUL PRESENT.

Like the RPG at the school festival.

EH HEH.

SH
YC
RE
PR
G
U
YO

LET'S TAKE A PICTURE WITH EVERYONE RIGHT NOW.

HANH?

YEAH. WE HAD SUCH A NICE ENDING AND ALL.

LAST PLACE.

...OH, WHO CARES ABOUT WHO'S LAST ANYMORE?

HUH?

Writing messages

I'VE DECIDED.

THEN LUCA-PYON AND YO-CHAN CAN ORDER MIKAN TO DO WHATEVER THEY WANT.

Whyyyyy?!

Why?!

MEEEEE?!

スタ
スタ...

That's great!

Wha?

RIGHT?

WAY TO GO, LUCA PYON! ☆

Hotaruuuu!

So I'm glad we got to let him have the spotlight, but...

I guess it's belated...

WELL...

IT IS HIS BIRTHDAY.

Good for you, Luca-pyon!

Shut up!

Don't call me Luca-pyon!

"YOU HAD BETTER WATCH OUT..."

"TRY NOT TO COLLECT ANY MORE LITTLE HANGERS-ON TO PROTECT."

...TIME WOULD STOP LIKE THIS...

IF ONLY...

Chapter 46 / End

Next time in

It's time for the Alice Academy Christmas party, and all the students are pitching in with their Alices to help with the preparations. But while Mikan has gotten a lot more comfortable with her own powers, how can "nullification" help in a situation like this? Meanwhile, the holidays are bringing up a variety of confusing emotions all around, and quite a bit of speculation about romance...

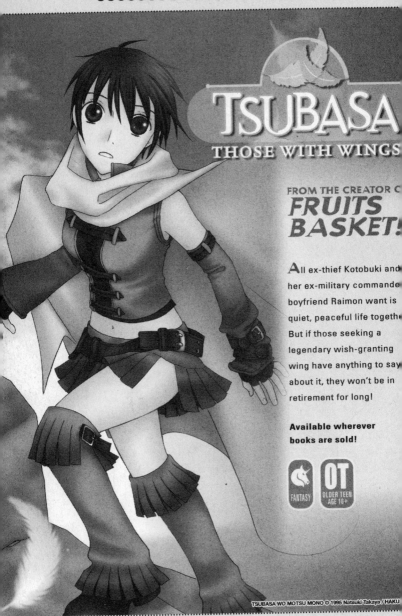

STOP!

This is the back of the book.
You wouldn't want to spoil a great ending!

This book is printed "manga-style," in the authentic Japanese right-to-left format. Since none of the artwork has been flipped or altered, readers get to experience the story just as the creator intended. You've been asking for it, so TOKYOPOP® delivered: authentic, hot-off-the-press, and far more fun!

DIRECTIONS

If this is your first time reading manga-style, here's a quick guide to help you understand how it works.

It's easy... just start in the top right panel and follow the numbers. Have fun, and look for more 100% authentic manga from TOKYOPOP®!